D1398873

The

Confidence

Cure

*7 FOUNDATIONS TO AN AGE-DEFYING BODY
UTILIZING ELECTRICAL FREQUENCIES AND
SIMPLE HOLISTIC SOLUTIONS*

Char

Copyright © 2020 Char Fontanills. All rights reserved. No part of this book can be reproduced in any form without written permission of the author and its publisher.

DEDICATION

This is dedicated to the love of my life, DJ,
who whispered in my ear every day that I had
a message to spread, and to the thousands of
women who have supported me and have
made it their mission to lovingly build
confidence in every woman they know.

Contents

ACKNOWLEDGMENTS

I want to thank my mom and dad for their encouragement, and for continually being my biggest cheerleaders and role models. Without them, I would never be who I am today.

To my friends, who surrounded me with love. To those who supported me and became my family in my darkest hours. You held me when I was falling.

To my COO and my dear friend, Andrea Mercury, whose passion for our mission is contagious, for her countless late nights working on our projects and for her support and guidance to our Bodicurrent™ Practitioners across the nation.

To the women who shared the vision of Confidence by Char to create confidence so strong that you are never too scared to "Be Seen." I adore all of you, and I appreciate your support in promoting our products and services to your clients. Without your trust in me and passion for our mission, none of this would have been possible.

You are my inspiration.

Love,

Char

PREFACE

Why am I in a bikini on the front of a book?

Nausea and complete doubt.

As I face the launch of this book, I am engulfed by fear at the sight of the cover.

I hear the words in my ear over and over from my first, abusive husband.

"Your body is disgusting."

"You need to cover up."

"You are fat."

"You are flabby."

"Your belly pokes out."

"You need a boob job."

"You need to work out."

"THAT'S what you are wearing?"

"Why can't you look like her?"

"You need more makeup."

"What's going on with your hair?"

Every single time I was disrobed for a bath and he happened to catch a glimpse, he would degrade me.

The lights were always out during sex.

It wasn't really sex, it was more like an unwanted invasion of my body.

I had no job.

No skills.

No college degree.

No future.

No hope.

I would suffer in silence. No one could know.

At 18 years old and 117 lbs., there is absolutely nothing wrong with my body.

Daily, he picked away at my confidence like a vulture, tearing away at my already delicate self-esteem. He was slowly devouring any glimmer of confidence that I had.

Verbal abuse was just the tip of the iceberg. If you are in an abusive relationship you know the drill.

You walk around with a painted smile and cautious movements, hoping that no-one can see the deteriorating soul happening inside of you.

His threats did not end with me.

He would convince me that if I told my family, he would burn their house down and it would be all because of me.

That fear haunted me daily.

My mom's home is her sanctuary.

My dad was a blue-collar, hard-working man his entire life. We survived on a very modest income. My parents followed a very strict budget and managed to always, creatively, make ends meet. My dad's goal was simple, to provide a safe home and to put food on the table for us.

His family was everything, and he would protect and provide, no matter what.

If my dad knew what was happening behind closed doors, it would only be a matter of moments before he would be here to confront my abuser. My biggest fear was what my ex would try to do to my dad. My dad is meek, quiet, gentle, and tolerant; until you mess with his family. He will defend his family without reservation.

That imagination kept me in prison.

By staying there and tolerating the abuse, I was protecting my family.

My family is my most valuable possession. I would allow nothing and no-one to harm my family.

I knew he was capable of violence after an incident that occurred one month after we were married. My parents came to check on us.   Little did they know what they were about to encounter: an irrational man who was drunk on control. He ordered them to go away, and when they refused, I thought he was leaving. Instead, he marched to his car, pulled out a gun, walked over to their new car and kicked out the back taillights. My mom gasped in disbelief and my father was about to lose control.

As I was screaming for my dad to stay calm, I was corralling my mom to stay inside, begging and pleading for peace. My ex erupted in a string of obscenities.

Just as fast as it began, he disappeared; leaving behind a ravenous black cloud from his screeching tires.

My dad consoled me and sat me down for a talk. "We can get an annulment. You don't have to stay here."

Back then my Christian beliefs were so embedded in me, that I could not conceive the idea of an annulment.

"No, I made the promise before God that this marriage was till death do us part, and I will keep my promise," I cried with scalding tears.

This is how my new marriage began. Over the 7 years, it would intensify. I would calculate and plot my way out.

What was meant for my harm would eventually lead to me transforming from a shy, timid, insecure girl into a powerful, empowered and dynamic woman.

A woman who would find her voice.

A woman that would eventually grow her courage.

A woman that would regain her confidence.

A woman that would start a successful Body Company.

A woman that would devote her life to encouraging other women

to find their voice

to find their courage

to find their BIG BOLD CONFIDENCE.

Courage doesn't mean without fear. It means DESPITE the fear.

So, did I have doubts in the middle of every night while I wrestled with the decision of whether or not to stand in a bikini on the cover of my first book for all to see?

Absolutely!

You can only lead where you are brave enough to go.

So, here I stand, in my Wonder Woman pose.

Brave.

Bold.

Courageous.

Come out of the shadows, despite the fear.

Join the movement of Confidence.

INTRODUCTION

The older I get, the more challenging it is to reach my goals. My confidence wanes, and I wish for that youthful body I once had.

I'm not ready to give up my cute clothes!!

I don't want to "dress my age!"

I find myself cringing at those ridiculous articles that say you should wear this in your 20s, this in your 30s, and basically put you in a drab, boxy, conservative outfit in your 50s, 60s and 70s!!

Who said you have to be invisible as you grow older?

In this book, you will discover my number one recommendation to hacking youth at a cellular level that will not only change your body visually, it will quickly become an integral part of your overall longevity plan. You will also discover the 7 foundational elements that you can implement immediately to begin your journey to support a youthful healthy body at every age.

I have over 30 years in the beauty industry, I have been a successful entrepreneur and investor for over 20 years, and I have empowered women around the country to be financially independent and thrive in their own businesses. The driving force behind all of these accomplishments has been my ability to grow through adversity and tragedy, and to come out on the other side shining with the hope of inspiring others.

After the unexpected loss of my husband, the end of my fairy tale life as I knew it, and an accident that threatened to disfigure my face permanently, my life would take an unexpected turn and my true life's mission would finally be revealed.

I am excited and honored to share with you the journey that would lead me to discover the fascinating world of electrical frequencies. This magical modality combined with other holistic solutions can have a profound effect on the body and your overall confidence.

I promise that by the time you finish this book, you will be inspired and know that you, too, have control over the vibrancy and youthfulness of your body.

- ✓ You CAN defy age.

- ✓ You CAN "Dare to be Seen" at every age and every stage of your life.

- ✓ May your light shine and may you never sit in a dark corner again.

Love,

Char

The Day That Stole My Confidence

*The most painful goodbyes are the ones that are
never said, never explained.*

~Unknown

The decorations are set!

Our Mexican fiesta is ready.

It's 3:30 on a Friday afternoon.

Margaritaville starts at 5:00.

Time to slip into a nice bath and primp a bit before 50 of my closest friends arrive to celebrate the beginning of a perfect weekend. I secretly have an ulterior motive for this party, which is to convince one of my friends to move to this heavenly town! But no matter the outcome, I am happy to celebrate with my friends on a Friday!

Colorado is stunning in June. The smell of wildflowers mingle with the freshness of the mountain air, the brisk cool streams flow and the brush of the wind against the warmth of the sunshine is magical. You just want to breathe and take it in. No wonder people visit Colorado in the summer and never go home.

I love throwing parties! The laughter and affection I share with my friends just feeds my soul. I get so giddy waiting for them to arrive.

George is supposed to be home today, but he called a few days ago to say he had a mild case of pneumonia.

"Don't worry honey, I have medication, it's mild and the doctor said rest a few days and then I can travel." he explained.

George has been traveling for 2 straight weeks.

He's in Singapore now. I begged to go on this trip with him. This is his third trip now to Singapore in a short amount of time. He has many new accounts there and has just finished wrapping up a pretty impressive training using algorithms and crazy strategies using numbers, graphs, and formulas. He reminds me of Albert Einstein, with his eccentric ideas at times, but this project has been different. He has spent the last 3 years developing it, and millions of dollars in the process. Finally, he proclaims, the fruit of his work is about to be revealed. We launch in two weeks!!!

I have never seen him so excited and so exhausted.

He has bags under his eyes, his health has deteriorated, and his eating habits are self-destructive. I can see the toll it has taken on his body in his weight gain and his physical appearance. Looking into his eyes, I can see how hollow they are; and I can see how he moves so slowly, as if the energy has drained completely out of him. I was secretly wondering, "how in the world could he do this trip?"

If I can go with him, I can take care of him.

My begging continues.

"Pleaseeeee George, take me with you."

"Why don't you want me to go?"

"No, honey," George responds, "I will be okay. I have way too much to do. Wait till the next time, we will plan it and I will have much more time to do something fun with you."

"But you need me," I insisted.

Still, he denies my request.

My heart is wilting. I really don't understand why he is so against it. He is usually so responsive to my every request. That's the one thing I love about George; his heart. Everything he has ever done has been with my good in mind. He says he wakes up every day and asks, "How can I make Char's life better?"

Sounds like a fairy tale and it is.

I'm excited for this party, but I'm also feeling an unexplained unease in my body. A cloud of worry lurks in the corners of my mind.

I received a text in the middle of the night from George. I was deep asleep and somehow, I missed it. He simply said, "I'm in the hospital. They can take better care of me here. I hate hospitals."

When I awoke the next morning, I frantically tried to reach him. First by text, then by phone so as not to wake him in the case that he was resting. "I shouldn't have been sleeping while he was in the hospital! How could I have missed this call? Is he okay?" I frantically thought to myself.

I begin dialing as quickly as I can. My heart is racing and all I need to do is just hear his voice and then everything will be okay.

Ring…. ring….. ring…….

I try again and again. No response. No answer. I haven't spoken to him in days. Now I missed his call from the hospital. I don't even know what hospital he is in! How can I not even know what hospital he is in?!!!!

"Why isn't he calling me, why isn't he responding to my texts? What is going on?" Hours go by, and my excitement to hear from him begins to turn to a restrained panic. My voice begins to quiver, and my stomach grows with a nauseating ache.

Olivia, my housekeeper, is here, helping to prep for the party. "George is fine, it will be better now, he will call you soon" she says reassuringly.

The phone rings. It's my mom. She can hear my voice trembling. "Char," she calmly asserts, "now that he is in the hospital, they can monitor him and keep him well. It's a good thing. He will get better now. He probably doesn't have his phone charger. He will call you when he can, after he rests. There is no need to worry."

I find comfort in her voice.

Yes, all will be better now.

I continue to decorate and get the food cooked.

Hours drag by. Time to get ready.

My bath is warm. I will soak and retreat.

All will be fine. As I prepare to disrobe and slip into the warm water, my cell rings abruptly.

I see it's from George!!!!

OMG I can feel the tension in my body release and at the same time my heart is racing, I leap towards the phone. I fumble clumsily in my attempt to grasp the phone and hear his voice.

"Honeyyyyyy!!!! OMG, I've been so worried!!!! Are you ok?!" I exclaim.

"HE'S GONE, HE'S GONE, HE'S GONE!!!"

I hear piercing screams on the other end of the phone. I can hear a woman with an Asian accent; a woman whose voice I don't recognize. She rambles a distorted explanation of where George is and I can hardly interpret what she is screaming to me.

Why does another woman have his phone?

How does she know his passcode?

Why is she calling me?

Why is she with him at the hospital?

I interrupt her and say, "What do you mean he's gone? WHERE IS HE? I WANT TO SPEAK TO HIM!?! WHY DO YOU HAVE HIS PHONE?!!!!"

She continues with a quivering, distraught, sometimes elevated voice. She's mumbling the same words over and over and I can't quite understand her.

Her mumbling suddenly turns to an outburst.

"GEORGE IS DEAD!"

"What?!!! I exclaim. "What are you saying?

Who the fuck are you?!!!!

If this were true, why isn't the hospital calling me?

Why are you doing this?!!!!"

I am shaking.

I don't believe her.

I take her number. I don't even know what to do next.

I don't understand why the hospital hasn't called me.

If the hospital hasn't called then it's not true.

Who is this woman who has his phone and his passcode to get into the phone?

I fall to the floor.

What do I do now?

Should I call someone?

I know this isn't real. Maybe I call my mom.
She will tell me if it's real.

No answer.

I leave a message, begging my mom to call
me immediately.

I try to control my voice. I don't want to
alarm her.

I call my best friend. She will know what to do. I am sure it's not true. She will help me know what to do next.

The phone rings and rings.

My voice is trembling more now.

I leave another message.

I try to stabilize my voice.

After all, this is a strange woman that called me.

I am certain she's mistaken.

I call another and another and another. After what seems like an eternity, I have called everyone I can think of. There is no one to call. No one can hear me. What do I do?

With each failed attempt, I lose my breath. I can no longer feel my hands. My knees are giving way to gravity. My heart is racing so fast; I lose sense of where I am.

I must stay present.

I must reach someone.

I can't see the numbers on the phone anymore.

Where is everyone??!!!

My mouth has lost the ability to move. I am floating in and out of consciousness. There is no one to come to my rescue.

Wails begin to bubble up from my belly, as if I am birthing a torturous pain I have never experienced before.

"Pleaseeeeee somebody help me!" I scream into the empty air.

I remember Michael, the store owner down the street called to find out about the party about an hour ago. Maybe he'll answer his phone. Maybe he is still at the store.

I ring him.

He answers. "MICHAEL, MICHAEL,

MICHAELLLLLLLL!!!!!!!"

I cannot get my mouth to form any other words.

"Char what is it? What's wrong?!!!" he exclaims.

"COME   MICHAEL   COME PLEASEEEEEEE COME!" I plead.

"I'll be there!" he shouts.

The next thing I remember is staggering out of my door and seeing Michael in the condo hallway.

My relief was so overwhelming, I collapsed at his feet.

When I awaken, I am on the couch in the living room; and 50 guests have arrived. Not to party, but to the shock of the death of my husband.

"I CAN'T DO THIS ALONE!!

I CAN'T DO THIS ALONEEEEEE!

PLEASEEEEEEE

IT'S A MISTAKE!

I'M SURE.

THE HOSPITAL HASN'T CALLED"

The weeks and months that followed brought brutal clarity. The fairy tale illusion was just an illusion.

The woman on the phone wasn't a co-worker as she explained herself. She was more than that and so were many others. I wasn't the only one in George's life and neither was she.

I thought our sexless marriage was because of his sexual inabilities. His lack of confidence. His health issues, his diabetes, his excessive weight gain, his stress and travel. Maybe it was some of that but that wasn't the whole story.

Why didn't he want me?

Why wasn't I enough?

What is wrong with me?

The questions and doubts flooded my mind.

I could feel my confidence vanishing.

Whatever relationships he had, I didn't want to know. No details. No anything.

I'm moving on.

I don't want to face reality.

I don't want to be shown the truth.

It's too painful for me.

I want to continue to live in the fairytale.

Little did I know, the damage was already done. I would doubt myself. I would harbor these secrets. I would tell no one that I was cheated on. They would know I wasn't enough. I wasn't enough for George, so I must not be enough for anyone else. They would think less of me, they would think less of George.

I felt like I had been caged.

Just a showpiece to his friends.

Just for the sake of being married.

I was so embarrassed and felt so ashamed.

My whole life felt like a lie.

I wanted revenge in a way. I hadn't been intimate with anyone in 5 years. I longed to be held and desired. In some strange way, I wanted to get revenge on George, even though I was mourning him. My heart literally hurt. The pain was so intense, I could hardly breathe at times. I felt like a butterfly that had finally been released but didn't know how to fly.

My self-confidence was destroyed, and I was not sure I had the fight to get it back.

Just when the caterpillar

thought her life was

over

she began to fly.

" I Have Plans For You"

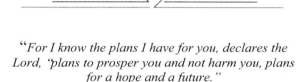

"For I know the plans I have for you, declares the Lord, "plans to prosper you and not harm you, plans for a hope and a future."

~Jer. 29:11

Ahhhhh…..February in Boulder, Colorado.

If you've never experienced Boulder weather, you are in for a treat.   The sun shines over 300 days a year. In February, you can experience dreamlike 50-degree weather which feels like a warm 70 with the dry climate.

With over 155 miles of hiking trails and 300 miles of assorted bike trails, it's a paradise for outdoor enthusiasts.

I'm biking today!

I have the cutest bike shorts and pink and black fitted bike shirt.   I have this stunning lightweight red road bike. I look hot and like a professional biker!

Even though it's only my third bike ride, I have managed to consistently bike 20 miles, each time! I feel so accomplished. I often watch the "big boys and girls" ride their road bikes along the trails in boulder, some of my best girlfriends ride up miles of incline to the top of mountain trails with their cute outfits and their rockin 'bodies. I want to be athletic. I want to have a rockin 'body. I want to get out of this fucking funk. I want the pain to stop, and I want to live again.

I am not sure it will ever happen, but if I keep trying, it will, right????

I'm riding with my boyfriend. I hesitate to call him that. Is it okay to fall in love and enjoy myself, even with my husband dead? I struggle with this.

Not sure if I can laugh.

Not sure if it's okay to live.

I feel there is a definite tug on my mind and body, sometimes struggling to stay present. I feel like my body is floating, and I am observing my body from above in a dreamlike state. I have no control and I just float through the days. I don't tell anyone. Sometimes, I tell my friend, who is also a therapist, and sometimes I tell my mom. I trust them both with everything, but even they don't know the extent of my tears. I cry every night for hours in the middle of the darkness, and every day when there is no one around. I lie there limp with no energy, and let the pain take over my body. I can't even move. I must gather enough energy to put on a happy face when DJ comes home, or when I see a friend.

I just closed George's business. After 8 months of fighting to keep it alive and make it a success, it was just over my head. It felt like another death. Now, he is truly gone, including his dream company that we spent millions and years developing; only to have it die with him just two weeks before launching.

I failed.

I failed him.

I failed everyone.

I wasn't even good enough to keep my husband loyal.

I can't do this.

I'm tired.

I'm so scared to even face life.

I feel like I am dying, too.

But I won't tell anyone. Not today.

Today I will ride my bike.

I will try.

It will get better, everyone says so.

It's gonna get better.

We are on the homestretch! I can feel the wind in my hair and just 2 miles from home! I'm actually laughing!

"Is it okay to laugh?" I ask myself quietly in my mind.

I recall the conversation I had with my mom just this morning. "It's okay to laugh again Char, it's okay to love, it's okay to live," she advises.

She's been encouraging me daily. Even when I wake up at 2:00 am with panic attacks, running to my closet, where my friends can't hear me cry and call my mom in overwhelming fear, she's there. She's always there.

I have 'round the clock care here. My friends rotate and stay every night. I don't quite understand this, I keep telling them I am fine, but they never leave me and I can't hide anywhere but in my closet in the middle of the night.

Mom compassionately listens, prays, encourages.

It's the only thing I find comfort in. After our two-hour-or-more nightly conversation, I sneak back into my bed, take some anxiety medication, and sleep.

If she wasn't here, I know I would die.

My heart hurts so badly. Please make it stop.

Will it ever stop hurting?

I won't tell anyone. When they ask, I will say, "I'm doing okay."

I've always laughed and smiled. I've always been a good girl. I can hide this. Someday, it will get better.

Today, I ride.

"Wheeeeeeee!!!" I squeal with joy. "This is so amazing!"

DJ is ahead of me leading the way. Suddenly an invisible car appears out of nowhere. She doesn't see me.

I abruptly jerk my bike out of her way but I'm going too fast. I fall off the edge of the road and instinctively jerk my bike back onto the pavement which is something you are never supposed to do.

DJ has told me repeatedly that if you fall off of the pavement, you must glide slowly back onto it. Never react with an abrupt jerk onto the pavement as it can cause a severe crash.

Every experienced rider knows not to do this. But I'm not experienced. My bike crashes with all the entire weight and force directly on my face. Even a helmet can't protect my tender white skin.

I manage to miss her car, but the crash is inevitable. I slide on gravel and rocks. My glasses are pressed into my face and even though shaken and embarrassed, I feel okay.

People are running and stopping on the highway. I try to move, and DJ stops me. "Stay here Char, we are going to take you to the hospital."

"Hospital???? NO, I am fine. Just give me a minute, I'm just a little shaky."

A Good Samaritan loads my bike and carefully helps me into his truck. "To the emergency room," DJ directs.

I continue to plead, "Please DJ you are overreacting. I'm just shaken, just give me a little while. I don't need a hospital." As I am shuffled into the truck, I glance into the driver's rear view mirror and for the first time I see the damage to my face. Suddenly the pain rushes in like a flood, and I feel like I am going to pass out. Blood is streaming down my face. I look at my torn gloves, bloody knuckles and ripped skin on my face and body. I feel light-headed. Nauseated. I can't breathe. I'm scared, but I will act calm.

"Just breathe Char" I whisper in my head.

8 hours later, I emerge.

"Broken in three places," the doctor reports.

"The orbital bone, the eye socket and the zygomatic bone, or cheekbone. We will need to schedule surgery within two weeks. We will place two metal plates in your face."

I listen. I have no intent on getting surgery. I will contact my close friend, Brandon, who I call my big brother in Miami. He's a top plastic surgeon there. I trust him. He will know what to do, but I don't need surgery.

After reviewing the x-rays, Brandon delivers the bad news. "Sis," he lovingly calls me, "you gotta have surgery. If you don't your face will continue to fall and you will become disfigured." My heart drops.

Over the course of the next week the entire left side of my face turns solid black-- from my forehead, all the way down to my neck -- from the impact of the fall. My face has doubled in size, with the swelling. My eye is completely red, with just a small opening to see. My vision is blurred. My will is broken. I feel defeated. I feel empty. I feel alone. I should have never had fun. I shouldn't have been laughing. I don't understand why God is punishing me.

I don't want to do this anymore.

What if I just went away?

Valentine's Day 2013.

Surgery day. I'm so scared, I can't stop crying. I feel so weak. I feel like I won't come back from this. I'm just floating and not really here.

The surgeons perform the reconstruction by opening up my face, and then put it back together in a way so it will hold, foregoing the use of facial plates. When they wake me from surgery and tell me this, I am shocked.

"I don't want a disfigured face, why didn't you put the plates in anyways, just to be certain?" I am trembling and choking back the tears. DJ assures me that I don't want plates in my face, but I am not convinced. I am worried it won't work.

For the next year, I follow all of the care instructions. I massage my face every day and nourish it with Vitamin C and other concoctions that I mix together in a desperation to make sure there are no scars. My skin heals perfectly with no visible damage, but there is definitely a droop on one side. I return to the doctors within the year and beg them to x-ray and put the plates in. They respond, saying my face is in place, it's just nerve damage and tissue loss. I leave defeated once again.

"Why did I have this stupid surgery if I was going to have a droop anyways?!!"

I meet with a friend who encourages me to explore microcurrent.

"It's used in rehab and even on people's faces after Bell's Palsy and many other instances involving muscle atrophy. It can really help you," he encourages.

I had just signed up for esthetics school the month prior to my bike accident. After closing George's business, I knew I needed to find something fun to do. Esthetics seemed easy. So, within one month of closing the business, I rushed to enroll in school. I had no intention of working, mind you, I just wanted to get my products at cost and learn all I could about keeping myself looking younger. Oh, and I thought it would be fun, and a way to get my mind off of all the trauma of the past year.

In class, the first month, they spoke about microcurrent and had an "expert" come to the school and speak to us about this modality. I remember being so coy, passing it off as rubbish. I stood up in class and publicly declared, "If you want to look younger you need Botox, filler and a great plastic surgeon, not microcurrent. That's the stupidest thing I have ever heard of!"

Fast forward exactly one month from enrolling in esthetics school and making fun of microcurrent, my accident occurred.

Here I am, years later, with a passion for electrical frequencies and their ability to change the face and body.

I started traveling around the U.S., visiting with machine creators, engineers and doctors. I tested and explored every microcurrent I could find. My goal was and still is to bring awareness to the power of frequencies and increase confidence on every level.

Foundation #1 - Biohacking the

Body with Frequencies

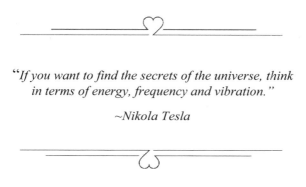

"If you want to find the secrets of the universe, think in terms of energy, frequency and vibration."

~Nikola Tesla

Microcurrent….. Reallyyyyy??!!!!

I never thought I would be interested in microcurrent. I never believed in anything holistic. Holistic to me always meant slow, ineffective, and some voodoo modality that didn't work.

I began my search into frequencies. The more I dug into the subject, the more fascinated and obsessed I became. I spent a ridiculous amount of money purchasing devices, in an attempt to heal my facial droop and change my body. I found out that microcurrent on the body can have a healing effect, even help with youthfulness of the body.

Since the accident, I had been getting everything from massage to dry needling to stop the pain in my back from the accident. Inflammation in my body due to the injuries was having a negative effect on my overall health. I researched thousands of articles and medical publications, day and night. I became somewhat of a lab rat, experimenting on my face and body.

While using different microcurrent frequencies to relax the muscles, I began to experiment on changing the shape and strength of my body using microcurrent. I discovered that microcurrent can not only reduce inflammation in the body but has been used for years by athletes in the know for improving physical stamina and strength. I also discovered that it has been used on the face for its anti-aging effects and even to increase collagen and elastin. I wondered what it could do for the look of the body.

Within a few months, I was seeing noticeable change. Friends began to ask me to give them treatments to which I replied, "I only do myself, I am not planning to do a business, but thank you for your interest."

Well, it didn't take long before I realized my "experiments" were costing tens of thousands of dollars and if they were willing to pay…. maybe I could consider a few clients to offset my purchases.

So, I began.

In my basement.

Experimenting on my face and body.

Testing day after day.

Then, opening my space to just a few clients.

By invitation only.

To the secret room in my basement.

Where I would transform many lives.

Word spread like wildfire.

By the end of the second month, I was booked solid.

I had no website.

I had no business card.

I had no menu of services.

My first year of business my annualized numbers were 6 figures and I didn't even feel like I was trying to do business.

It was then that I thought, maybe I need to share this on a bigger scale.

By then, my research had led me to an engineer that I developed a friendship with. I asked him to meet me in Vegas after a convention. I had an idea and wanted to get his feedback.

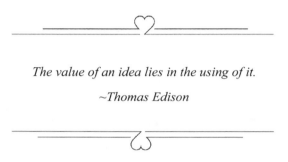

The value of an idea lies in the using of it.
~Thomas Edison

By the end of a 3-hour dinner and way too many margaritas, I had an unquenchable desire to build a machine. Custom designed. The best on the market. Built specifically for the body. I would hire him as my engineer and manufacturer. No expense would be spared, and we would build it from scratch.

Facial microcurrent devices were a dime a dozen on the market, but no-one had really specialized in microcurrent for the body. Non-surgical procedures have soared to a billion-dollar industry in just the last few years. With the majority of those procedures involving killing the fat by means of freezing it to death or heating it to dissolve it. These methods seemed very attractive to me as I struggled with my body issues, but I wanted a method that I could use over and over to assist me when my body shape fluctuated. Killing fat somehow seemed aggressive and not healthy to me. There had to be a better way!

Sometimes my stomach pooches out. The older I get, the harder it is to maintain a flat stomach, lean body, and youthful look to the skin on my body.

While pouring over countless research articles, I became more and more intrigued about using microcurrent on the body regularly. There have been many articles written about the advantages of microcurrent, most of which are written about the face. I wondered what all could be achieved if we specialized in using this modality on the body? What kind of impact could be attained on the youthfulness of the skin and cellular health of the body?

First of all, we must note that the body is electric.

Electricity is everywhere, even in the human body. Our cells are specialized to conduct electrical currents. The elements in our bodies, like sodium, potassium, calcium, and magnesium, have a specific electrical charge. Almost all of our cells can use these ions to generate electricity.

The use of electrical frequencies has been around since the end of the 19th century-- almost a hundred years after Luigi Galvani discovered that electricity can make the muscle in a frog's leg twitch. Subsequent research in electrophysiology has been carried out by people such as Robert O. Becker, Dr. Björn Nordenström, a former chair of the Nobel Selection Committee for Medicine, and Dr. Thomas Wing, who invented some of the first microcurrent devices.

Through the years, there have been an immense amount of devices created for medical purposes and for the esthetics markets which have all had varying degrees of efficiency and controversy.

One such researcher in the medical community made huge strides in the study of the effects of electrotherapy type devices. While this is a different type of device than we are speaking of, the development and use of these electrical modalities is quite interesting.   Dr. Bjorn Nordenstrom developed electrochemical therapy (EChT), a minimally invasive electrotherapeutic technique for the treatment of cancer and hemangioma tumors.   His theories and clinical results were not limited to cancer but encompassed many other areas of wound-healing.   It's an example of how the wide range of frequencies and electrical energy are being used in the body.

How do we create energy in the body?

Mitochondria are responsible for this process.

Mitochondria are organelles that float freely within the cell. Some cells have thousands of Mitochondria, and some have none. Muscle cells need more mitochondria, whereas the neurons (cells that transmit nerve impulses), don't need as many. The mitochondria act like a digestive system, which takes in nutrients, breaks them down, and creates energy-rich molecules for the cell. The biochemical processes of the cell are known as cellular respiration.

The energy that the Mitochondria produce is called Adenosine Triphosphate (ATP).

ATP is often referred to as the "energy of life." Every cell, every bodily function-- from the brain, to your heartbeat, to movement, digestion, regeneration of the skin and cells --every function of life in your body runs on the fuel called ATP.

You can survive without food for around 20-30 days, before bodily functions begin to shut down. You can survive without water for around 6 days, but you can only survive without ATP for 6 seconds.

- ➢ Without it, you die.

- ➢ As you age, you produce less of it.

- ➢ As illness occurs, it declines.

Microcurrent has been proven to increase ATP or adenosine triphosphate by up to 500%, helping you make energy more quickly and stimulating tissue and cellular repair.

So, how does microcurrent work?

Microcurrent therapy sends low-level electrical currents into your skin that are nearly identical to the body's own natural electrical frequencies. Running current over your body adds more electrons to your system, stimulating your body to repair more quickly and increases cellular health.

The interest in electrical frequencies and microcurrent are popular in the esthetics industry, as well with many celebrities touting the effects of using low electrical current on the skin. With such stellar results as increased ATP production, increased collagen and elastin, and muscle strength resulting in improved tone and tightness of the skin it's no wonder why it has gained such a notable following. Increased ATP is one of the most notable benefits of using this modality.

Microcurrent treatments for the face are performed by trained estheticians. There are devices for home use, such as Nuface or ZIIP. These should be considered for a slight touch-up for home use, but not for professional type results. A handheld home use device can't possibly compare with the results you get from a medical-grade commercial device. Don't be scared to ask the name of the microcurrent device that is used. Believe it or not, some luxury spas give a facial with a handheld, battery-operated, microcurrent device and call it a professional service. Some charge upwards of $350-$500 or more for the session.

Don't be fooled. This is fine for a fluffy facial where you need to look lifted and glowing for a day or so. For serious results, you will want to be treated by a professional, using a commercial type device. A series of sessions performed twice a week is recommended, or until the desired outcome is achieved. This translates to about 10-20 sessions (depending on age and health habits).

I am always asked, "Is this permanent?"

The answer is no. Remember we always have two enemies working against us which are aging and gravity. Nothing is permanent, but you can certainly slow the process. Think of it as going to the gym. It takes commitment, several times a week, to build muscle and make lasting change in the body. Then, once you achieve your goal, you must do regular care and maintenance. It's no different with these modalities. Even plastic surgery is not permanent, as long as we age and have gravity in the world.

Depending on lifestyle and health habits, microcurrent treatments are suggested every 4 - 6 weeks for maintenance. Smoking, alcohol consumption, lifestyle and your age can alter this recommendation. Your skin care professional will know what to recommend to you.

When using microcurrent on the face, the face is first prepared and cleaned thoroughly. Then, a conductive-type gel is applied for glide and for conductivity of the current. Professional face devices use metal probes that glide over the skin, using swiping and holding techniques to strengthen and work on the muscle area.

The effects of increased ATP for the face are apparent in photos. Many clients experience a youthful look to the skin, increased collagen production, elastin and many other youthful side effects. Some even look as though a face lift has been performed, and yet, it was the body's own ability to repair and restore creating that youthful look to the face.

Can microcurrent be used on the body? YES!!!

Bodicurrent™ is the name of our proprietary body service using microcurrent on the body. We have found it highly effective, and our treatment sets us apart from the many microcurrent services on the market. Be sure and ask for it by name to be assured you are having a true Bodicurrent™ signature treatment.

When a Bodicurrent™ signature treatment is performed, electrode pads are placed on the areas of concern. We concentrate on certain muscle groups, like the abdomen or the buttocks. These pads are made of soft fabric with an adhesive on one side and a metal connection on the other side.

The pads are simply peeled off the plastic-holding sheet and applied directly to the skin. The metal connection on the pad is connected to a positive and negative lead that is plugged into the microcurrent device. A low level electrical current flows from the device to the area where the pads are placed on the client's skin.

Microcurrent treatments are painless and require no down time which make them an ideal treatment for clients who wish to have holistic, non-invasive, yet effective body treatments. The sensation felt during a microcurrent treatment is similar to a TENS unit.

You may be familiar with a TENS unit as it is frequently used by a chiropractor to relieve pain. Now there are even TENS units you can purchase for home use.

When using a TENS unit, you will experience a slight buzzing sensation. This is quite similar to the feeling produced by Microcurrent but with extremely different results.

A TENS unit uses a milliamp of electrical current and targets the sensory receptors, sending a signal to block pain messages that are trying to reach the brain. This makes it a very effective tool for chiropractic use to help prepare the body for an adjustment.

A microcurrent device delivers a subsensory micro amperage current that is 1000 times less than the milliamperage current used in a TENS device.

The key benefit of TENS unit is blocking pain.

The key benefits of microcurrent are to boost collagen and elastin production and increase ATP production which can benefit every cell in the body.

Microcurrent, in published studies, has been shown to increase ATP production in the body by up to 500% and is a vital component to a youthful regimen.

Bodicurrent™ treatments use several combinations of specific microcurrent frequencies. Our medical-grade machine is a class 2 device for cosmetic use. It has 16 ports and has the ability to use up to 32 electrodes on the body. We can treat up to three body parts, simultaneously, for a full body transformation.

Sessions usually last 30-45 minutes and are performed twice weekly, for one to two months, or until desired results are achieved. The treatment is pain free, non-invasive, and completely holistic.

Another advantage of these treatments is you may repeat them over and over without any harm to the body. In fact, we recommend that you consider Bodicurrent™ signature treatments at least once a month as part of your age-reversal routine.

During a Bodicurrent™ signature treatment you may experience involuntary muscle contractions depending on the intensity your provider uses. This can also be performed where there is no contraction at all. You may also see redness on the skin once the pads are removed. This is totally normal due to the increased circulation in the area and generally goes away within 30 minutes.

This increased circulation is another advantage of these treatments. Circulation has many health benefits which include increased organ function and toxic waste removal from the body.

It is also believed that increased circulation can help with cellulite reduction, which is why we love these treatments on areas like the legs and buttocks.

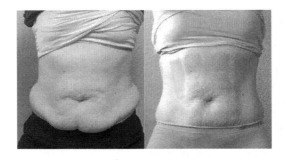

Actual results over a 6-8 week period of time.

Results may vary depending on age, lifestyle, health, and other factors.

*special note: red marks in after photo are where the pads were placed for treatment indicating increased circulation to the area. Redness will fade in about 30 minutes or so.

(Photo credit: Andrea Mercury - The Confident Body Boulder, Co)

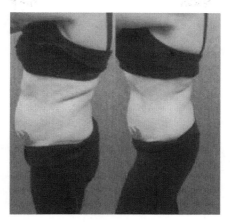

Actual client. Results may vary based on age, lifestyle, health and other factors.

Photo Credit: Amy Costello-Bowen

Baby Face Skin and Body- Denver, Co

When you look for a wellness center or professional to begin your microcurrent body treatments, look for a location that has a device with the ability to use 32 pads or more. Some devices on the market have 4 -8 portals, using only 16 pads or less. More coverage means more current running through the body; and more areas can be treated at once, to create a full body experience.

Over the years, looking at hundreds of photos, I am fascinated with what can happen to the look and feel of the skin.

Our clients have reported the skin appearing more youthful, tighter, lifted, and more beautiful than ever. Muscle strength, endurance, stamina, and overall tone were just a few of the reported effects of the treatments.

In Foundation #4, we will cover how applying our proprietary Bodicurrent™ signature treatment on the body can be combined with other modalities such as LED light therapy, cryotherapy, and infrared saunas.

What was most astonishing was the discovery that using the treatments on the *body seemed to have a profound effect on the appearance of the face.*

Applying microcurrent to the face produces some beautiful results, but what would happen to the face if we treated only the body? Could body treatments make the face look younger?

It makes logical sense that when you run a low electrical microcurrent through the body, it would not just be localized to the treated area, and it would affect the entire body from head to toe. Sounds great, but would it really show up in the face as well?

With photos like this, it's a definite YES!

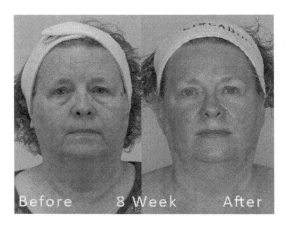

Photo credit: Holly Tanella

BoHo Alternative Med Spa - Allen, Texas

- ✓ **She did not have a medical procedure.**
- ✓ **She did not even have microcurrent on the face.**

96

✓ **She only had Bodicurrent™ treatments on the body!!**

Bodicurrent™ treatments had a profound effect on the look of her face!

We noticed reduced inflammation in the facial features, and the skin appeared much younger. She had a series of 16 Bodicurrent™ signature treatments over an eight-week period. During that time, she also had regular facials using skin care products, but no microcurrent on the face.

As you can see in the photos, her face looks as though she has had some type of procedure done on her face. Bodicurrent™ treatments can have an all-over youthful effect, from head to toe!

Fascinating, isn't it?

So began the quest to turn back the hands of time that were once only reserved for the face. Now there was a plan for a youthful body.

Remember the two enemies, aging and gravity, that are working on our youthful appearance at all times?

These two foes make maintenance a must and a part of life. A regular schedule of Bodicurrent™ treatments is important to keeping your youthful look and will vary based on age and lifestyle. If your budget allows you to go weekly, we believe that would be the ultimate youth preserving routine and the best solution for ongoing cellular health.

You can find a trained certified professional for Bodicurrent™ treatments on our website: https://www.confidencebychar.com.

Bodicurrent™ treatments are safe for most healthy individuals, but there are some contraindications. You will be asked to fill out a health questionnaire to find out if you are qualified. If there is any question, your professional will provide you with the necessary document to get approval from your family doctor.

FAST FACTS ABOUT
BODICURRENT™ Treatments

- ✓ Bodicurrent™ uses microcurrent which increases ATP production by up to 500%

- ✓ Benefits of Increased ATP is collagen and elastin necessary for youthful skin

- ✓ Bodicurrent™ treatments using microcurrent increases stamina, endurance and strength and can be used for building muscle and tone of the body

- ✓ Building muscle strengthens your metabolism which is helpful in maintaining and achieving a healthy weight.

- ✓ Bodicurrent™ treatments do not replace exercise as we all know the benefits of exercise for keeping the body youthful and healthy.

- ✓ Bodicurrent™ treatments are recommended to amplify your diet and exercise efforts and support cellular health.

Our mission at Confidence by Char is to provide you with breakthrough treatments, luxury supplements and purpose-driven products for your mind and body. We are committed to providing services that evoke so much confidence you will proudly walk out your door and showcase your masterfully crafted body at every age and stage of your life.

Do we have all the studies needed to PROVE that using microcurrent is the key to a more youthful body, or that our device is the key to cellular health and a youthful looking body at every age? The answer is no. In theory, it works. In photos, we see a difference. A significant difference. While others wait for "studies," I'll just keep looking younger and loving my body!

Foundation #2 - Is WATER the Secret?

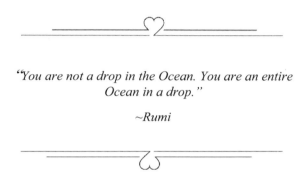

"You are not a drop in the Ocean. You are an entire Ocean in a drop."

~Rumi

Want to look younger?

> ➤ Drink water

Relieve Stress?

> ➤ Drink water

Lose weight?

> Drink water

Digestive problems?

> Drink water

Lubricate your joints?

> Drink water

Remove toxins?

> Drink water

Prevent kidney damage?

> Drink water

Help your brain function?

> Drink water

Protect tissues, spinal cord?

> Drink water

Feeling tired?

> Drink water

In fact, all bodily functions are dependent on this clear priceless liquid.

Water is a treasure and so neglected by so many.

Did you know that even mild dehydration can cause a spike in cortisol levels?

Apparently, a really great and really cheap fix for stress is a simple glass of cool water. The lack of it puts undue stress on the organs and causes cortisol to rise. Cortisol is known as the stress hormone. It is produced by the adrenal glands. When cortisol is released into the bloodstream, it raises the body's metabolism of glucose. Cortisol also aids adipocytes (baby fat cells) to grow into mature fat cells. Pair this dehydration, stress, raised cortisol levels, and the need to reach for a piece of chocolate cake when stressed; and you can wreak havoc on your ability to zip your skinny jeans. Makes me think twice about what I really need when I am feeling stressed. Perhaps a tall glass of spa water is the ticket. (Recipe suggestions at the end of this chapter.)

Water, or lack of water, also affects your cognitive function. Even mild dehydration produces alterations in a number of important aspects of cognitive function; such as concentration, alertness, and short-term memory. With the brain and heart being made up of 73% water, we are literally starving our brains of the necessary fuel to function at optimum levels. Over time, can you imagine the effect of this slow drain on the brain?

There are a million reasons for joint pain. However, did you know there is a common thread in many situations of joint pain? Ineffective synovial fluid. Synovial fluid is a liquid cushion in the joints that reduces friction and provides resistance to impact. When there is not enough liquid, joints become painful. The most common reason for synovial failure? Dehydration.

FACTS ABOUT WATER AND YOUR BODY

- ✓ The body is 60% water and 71% of the earth is covered in water.

- ✓ The brain and heart are composed of 73% water

- ✓ The lungs are about 83% water

- ✓ The skin contains 64% water

- ✓ Muscles and kidneys are 79% water

- ✓ Even the bones are watery at 31%

- ✓ WATER is essential for life.

- ✓ NON-NEGOTIABLE

Kidney health is dependent upon water. Water carries wastes from the blood to the kidneys. Water keeps the blood vessels open so they can carry nutrients to the bloodstream. Mild dehydration can cause you to become tired, and more severe dehydration can cause kidney damage.

What about youthful skin? Models know this secret. They drink water, and lots of it. The structure of the skin and the cells to produce collagen depend on water.

✓ Water is not a choice, as many of us think it is.

✓ You will die from no food in about 20-30 days.

- ✓ You will die from dehydration in about 6 days.

- ✓ Water is even more important to life than food.

Yes, water is a vital nutrient essential to the life of every cell. It not only regulates our internal body temperature by sweating, but it also assists in flushing waste and toxins from the body. The carbohydrates and proteins that our body uses as food are metabolized and transported by water in the bloodstream.

Magic pill?

Secret potion?

YES!!!!

Readily available and very, very, cheap.

Water is also a key ingredient when performing treatments using electrical frequencies such as microcurrent for face or body or the coveted Bodicurrent™ signature treatments.

Think of it this way, the fastest way for an electrical current to flow is through water. Water is the conduit. Drop a live electric cord in water, and the current travels freely. Drop it on a wood floor, and nothing happens.

A hydrated cell becomes the conduit for the low electrical frequencies to flow and be effective in the body. Without hydration it becomes a dud. That is the reason we have our clients drink at least half their body weight in water, prior to treatment on the face or the body. It is a determining factor in a successful treatment using microcurrent or when having Bodicurrent™ treatment.

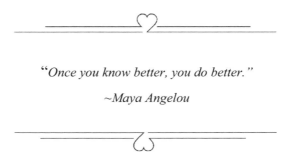

"Once you know better, you do better."
~Maya Angelou

Now you know.

Today is that day.

Vow to begin today.

Fall in love with water and what it does for your most valuable possession, your body.

Half your body weight in ounces every day is a great start. Increase that amount if you drink coffee, tea or alcohol. For example, for every cup of coffee or alcohol, you should drink two cups of water to offset the diuretic effects, less if you are drinking tea. For those of us that have a challenge drinking plain water, there are so many flavored waters on the market. Just make sure you make a choice without added sugars or artificial flavorings.

An economical and delicious way to drink water is to flavor it yourself. There are tons of recipes for flavored water. No need to measure. Just pick your favorites and make up some of your own. Drop ingredients into a gallon of water and store overnight in the fridge. If you have never liked water, a few of these combinations may get you hooked.

Here are just a few of my favorite spa water recipes. Take these ideas and mix them up to create your own unique recipes!

- ➢ Strawberries and Cucumber
- ➢ Strawberries and Mint
- ➢ Strawberries and Basil
- ➢ Mint and Cucumber
- ➢ Lemon and Cucumber
- ➢ Cucumber and Mint
- ➢ Cucumber and Lime
- ➢ Chopped Fresh Basil
- ➢ Watermelon and Mint
- ➢ Watermelon and Basil
- ➢ Pineapple and Ginger
- ➢ Pineapple and Orange
- ➢ Orange and Fennel
- ➢ Peach and Cinnamon Sticks

- Lemons and Lavender
- Grapefruit
- Apple, Lemon, and Cinnamon Sticks
- Red Raspberries and Rosemary
- Red Raspberries and Orange
- Cantaloupe
- Blueberry and Pear
- Kiwi and Cucumber
- Blackberry and Orange
- Apple and Cinnamon Sticks
- Grapefruit and Mint
- Cranberry
- Celery
- Tomato and celery

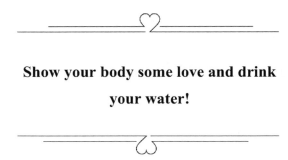

Show your body some love and drink your water!

Foundation #3 - Fat Is A Beautiful Thing.

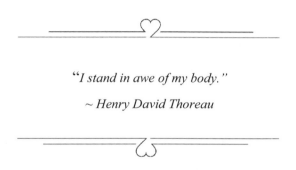

"I stand in awe of my body."

~ Henry David Thoreau

YOUR body is a masterpiece.

Some of us have the perception that fat is an ugly substance in the body that you want less of, and if you can rid of it forever it is a dream come true!

I remember when liposuction became popular in the early '80s. I thought, "wow" this is the most amazing invention ever! We can get our fat sucked out and have a perfectly sculpted body!

Seemed way too good to be true, because it was.

There is growing research that shows fat is an organ. You heard that right. Fat is an organ! Just like any organ of the body, it has an amazing and integral role to play. One of my favorite books on this subject is "The Secret Life of Fat" by Dr. Sylvia Tara. I encourage you to explore her research further.

To understand fat, let's first take a look at its structure. What exactly is fat, and what role does it actually play in the body?

Fat gets a bad rap and it is seen as the enemy. It jiggles, it hangs over our jeans, we grab it, curse it and wish it were gone. We beat it up, brush it, cup it, massage it, freeze it, burn it, suck it, perform an exorcism, and send it to hell.

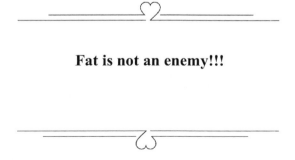

Fat is not an enemy!!!

The more you know about fat, my hope is you learn to appreciate it and desire to manage it, rather than destroy it.

Fat is important.

Fat is composed of tissue called adipose. Its main role is to store energy, but it also cushions the body and regulates temperature.

Adipose is made up of individual fat cells called adipocytes.

Mammals have two types of adipose or fat stored in the body.

White fat and brown fat.

White fat provides insulation for the body and serves as a storage tank for energy. When you exert a lot of energy or your body feels its starving, it reaches into this reserve and fat burning begins. White fat can easily be found. If you grab the inch that spills over your jeans, that's white fat.

Brown fat, or brown adipose tissue (BAT), stores energy in a smaller space than white fat. It's packed with iron-rich mitochondria, which is how it gets its color. When brown fat burns, it creates heat without shivering. This process is called thermogenesis. During this process, the brown fat also burns calories. The more brown fat you have, the better you are at burning calories.

How do you get more?

Some believe that exposure to cold could increase brown fat cells. We will explore this more in Foundation 4: Let There be Light, Fire and Ice.

Brown fat is located in very weird places, like the back of the neck or in the shoulders. It isn't located in the same place on everybody. Sometimes brown fat is mixed in with white fat, which is one more reason why you may want to think twice about killing or sucking out the fat in your body. You may be killing those very treasured brown fat cells.

I've never been so in love with the color brown!

What I found most interesting is that the soft tissue surrounding our body is only about three-quarters fat, with the rest composed of collagen fibers, veins, nerves, stem cells, immune cells and blood. Collagen fibers help hold the skin in place (excerpt from "The Secret Life of Fat" by Dr Sylvia Tara).

I like to think of it as the netting that holds to skin taut and gives it buoyancy. Without it, the skin would begin to sag and become loose.

There are many non-invasive techniques on the market today that claim to not harm the body. If fat is an organ and holds powerful stem cells within it, as well as immune cells, fibroblasts, collagen fibers that keep the skin in place, and even hormones involved in metabolism; what visual effects do you think it will have on the skin, if you removed it by killing it or sucking it out of the body?

What are the effects on the skin, when disrupting and destroying the collagen fibers that are contained in our valuable fat layer?

In the white fat layer, hormones are also produced. White fat also contains certain hormones such as adiponectin, and leptin, that are involved in regulating fat.

Adiponectin is a hormone that modulates where our fat is stored.

The hormone leptin is produced by fat cells. Leptin is a cell-signaling hormone vital in the regulation of appetite, food intake, and body weight. Studies have shown that an absence of leptin in the body, or leptin resistance, can lead to uncontrolled feeding and weight gain.

Fat also plays a role in fertility. You may know this to be true if you have ever tried to get pregnant. If your body fat falls below 18%, you may have difficulty conceiving. So, fat really isn't an enemy. It's a vital component of a healthy body.

I am a real woman with real concerns when it comes to my body. I am over the age of 55, and I went through menopause at 40. I have struggled with weight and hormonal balances, ever since that time. Many of my friends have also struggled with a slower metabolism and balancing the ever-changing landscape of hormones. I can tell you without a doubt, that if most women knew that killing or sucking out fat from the body would disrupt our hormonal balance and affect our metabolism, we would never choose to remove fat from the body!

A better plan, in my opinion, is to become friends with our fat. Think of ways to burn fat as energy and manage the fat and the body through good nutrition, movement and body hacks to support body functions.

If you are one of the millions of people who have removed fat from your body through liposuction or freezing or heating the fat to its death, and you have had great results, good for you. In my opinion, killing fat is not a solution to long term fat management. I would not recommend this type of treatment over and over.

Traumatizing the tissue could be counterproductive to the youthfulness, elasticity, and overall health of the skin and body.

Instead, look for alternative body hacks and solutions to supporting the body's production of collagen, elastin, ATP and more as discussed in Foundation #1 using Bodicurrent™ treatments or microcurrent treatments and, in Foundation #4, the effects of LED light therapy, cryotherapy, and infrared saunas. Consider time-restricted eating windows or intermittent fasting as discussed in Foundation #5. Seek out solutions to support the health of the skin, body, and your fat. Look at fat as a vital component of your body instead of a disgusting enemy to pluck out, torture, or destroy.

So, what's a girl to do!!!!?

I JUST WANNA WEAR MY SKINNY JEANS AGAIN!!

I work hard, and I play hard. When I play, it may be an extended vacation or enjoying a fine meal or wine with friends. I indulge, with moderation, but I indulge and enjoy experiences including food. How many times have you vacationed or indulged, only to return home with an extra 5lbs to 10lbs?

This cycle happens to me a lot!

When I come home, I want the bulge gone and gone FAST!

This is where alternative solutions can come in handy. Solutions that can be repeated over and over.

The foundational ideas discussed in this book can support your efforts and can be added to your secret arsenal of body-beautification tools. It's all part of a youthful recipe. Each ingredient or step discussed here builds upon the next. The exciting news is that there are many holistic solutions to support you in your quest for a youthful, lean, beautiful body. Here, we present you with a few central ideas. Continue to build upon these and enjoy the results.

Foundation #4 - Let There Be Light, Fire and Ice

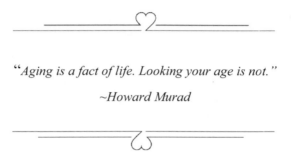

"Aging is a fact of life. Looking your age is not."

~Howard Murad

LED Light Therapy

A powerful three-part punch to add to your youthful preservation toolbox is LED light therapy, infrared saunas, and cryotherapy.

LED light therapy, or Light Emitting Diode, is a painless, non-invasive treatment that has been shown to rejuvenate the skin by increasing the elasticity and luminosity and stimulates collagen production.

The treatment uses varying light waves including red, blue, and yellow. It was originally created by NASA for plant growth on shuttle missions.

It has also been used to speed wound healing and for acne treatment. The same benefits that LED light therapy gives to the face can be applied to the body. Most LED light devices are small and used on the face. Recently more companies are realizing the demand for a youthful looking body and are now producing "Light Beds," full body LED light therapy beds.

The key to this modality is consistency. If you are using one of the many hand-held, home-use type devices, most can be used 5-7 times a week. Always follow manufacturer suggestions. For professional treatments done at high end spas or dermatology offices you will likely start with a series, and depending on skin care goals and concerns, you will be seen once a week for a number of months. This will depend on different manufacturers and your specific desires or needs. Some of my personal favorites are Lightstim, Lightwave, and Joovv.

Infrared saunas

Infrared saunas are a fantastic body treatment. Unlike a traditional sauna, which heats the air around you, infrared saunas penetrate human tissue and heat your body before heating up the air. Sunlighten and Jacuzzi are just a few of the popular brands. According to Jacuzzi, near infrared is a shorter wavelength and will be absorbed just below the surface of the skin creating a sweat that promotes healing and revitalization. Mid infrared is a longer wavelength that can penetrate deeper into the body's soft tissue increasing circulation, releasing oxygen to reach injured areas. Far infrared is the longest wavelength, which penetrates the fat cells causing vasodilation, where the fat cells vibrate to expel toxins, resulting in the greatest levels of detoxification and stimulate your metabolism to aid in weight-loss. Full spectrum infrared saunas incorporate all three wavelengths, as a result you get a full range of health benefits.

My favorite infrared sauna company is Sunlighten. Sunlighten was founded as a result of a personal healing experience with infrared therapy. For more than a decade, founder Jason Lincoln Jeffers suffered from chronic illness and relied on traditional medicine to manage his condition. It was only when he discovered infrared saunas that he truly began to heal. Jason founded Sunlight Saunas (now Sunlighten) in 1999 to make more people aware of the remarkable healing power of infrared that he, personally, experienced. Today, the company continues to innovate even greater technologies with the goal of bringing products that empower wellness into homes and businesses around the world.

Cryotherapy

Cryotherapy, often referred to as whole-body cryotherapy, is the latest trend in body hacking. This is a method where you are exposed to extremely cold air for several minutes. You enter into an enclosed chamber with an opening at the top for your head. You stand in the enclosure for up to 3 minutes, exposing your body to negative 200-300 degrees Fahrenheit. The results are best when done regularly, as with any of these modalities.

The FDA has not approved any whole-body cryotherapy device as safe and effective to treat medical conditions, and the American Academy of Dermatology doesn't recommend whole-body cryotherapy. They call whole body cryotherapy a "growing trend."

Purported benefits include:

- ✓ May support weight loss

- ✓ Reduced inflammation

- ✓ Pain relief

- ✓ May speed athletic recovery

- ✓ Reduced anxiety and depression, and many others, but more research is needed to support those claims.

Well, "growing trend" or not, I love and engage in these treatments regularly. I have personally experienced the amazing benefits. I love the way cryotherapy makes me feel. I feel invigorated, wide awake, and so refreshed. It feels like I could go out and conquer the world. Though much more research needs to be done to support the idea of possible weight loss, there are a few studies that show that regular exposure to cold changes the metabolic response.

Some believe that cold exposure can lead to development of more brown fat. As discussed in Foundation #3, brown fat burns more calories. Sign me up! Brown may be my new favorite color!

Foundation #5 - The Longevity Hack

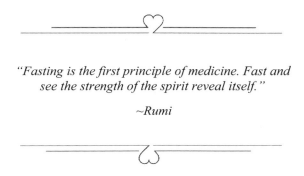

"Fasting is the first principle of medicine. Fast and see the strength of the spirit reveal itself."

~Rumi

I grew up fasting. It was a way to be silent, pray and get closer to God. Denying the flesh, in order to gain a deeper spiritual connection, gave me more clarity; and I was able to listen to my inner voice or hear guidance whispered in my ear.

Fasting has taken on new meanings and is all the rage now for its health benefits. So, whether you do it as a spiritual awakening or to hack your body into a healthier state, fasting is a powerful tool; both physically and mentally.

Fasting is possibly one of the cheapest body hacks for longevity.

Longevity is having a chronic disease and taking care of it.

~Oliver Wendell Holmes

Calorie restriction, intermittent fasting, and even limiting the time at which you eat has been shown to influence health markers such as cancer and diabetes, even having an impact on age-related illnesses.

Fasting, particularly extended fasting, can trigger a process called autophagy (self-eating).

Through autophagy, the body cleans out the damaged cells and toxins and replaces them with fresh new healthy cells. When you are younger, your body is more efficient at cleaning out the dead, toxic and damaged cells; but as we age, once again, things slow down. This process can slow aging, reduce inflammation, and even support your body to perform at a higher level.

It sounds like a horror movie that your cells are self-eating mechanisms, but it's actually very powerful.

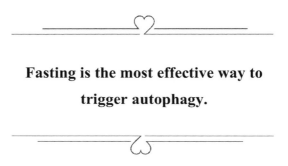

Fasting is the most effective way to trigger autophagy.

Fasting is the most effective way to trigger autophagy, it's easy and I feel I am supporting my cellular health.

How long do you fast before achieving autophagy? It's really not a clear-cut answer. A study was done, but it was done with mice that showed it began after 24 hours of fasting. As interest grows, more studies will be done; and perhaps we can get better answers. Numbers range from 48-72 hours.

One well known proponent of fasting is Dr. Jason Fung. His book, "The Complete Guide to Fasting", written along with Jimmy Moore, has gained quite a following.

I regularly do fasts. My routine is time-restricted eating windows on a daily basis and regular fasts ranging from 1 to 3 days, each quarter. There is no steadfast rule. Experiment, and see what works for your body and lifestyle. I find fasting improves my mental clarity and overall health. Consult with a health professional to see if this might be an option for you.

Foundation #6 - The Power of "I AM"

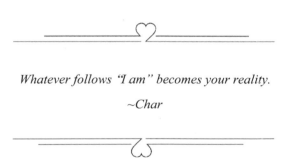

Whatever follows "I am" becomes your reality.

~Char

Two words that will change your life.

I AM.

Throughout the years, I have said some stupid things.

- ➤ "I am looking older."
- ➤ "I am not able to do what I used to do."
- ➤ "I am slow."
- ➤ "I am unworthy."
- ➤ "I am fat."
- ➤ "I am ugly."
- ➤ "I am getting sick."
- ➤ "I am forgetful."
- ➤ "I am shy."
- ➤ "I am poor."
- ➤ "I am not good enough."
- ➤ The list goes on and on.

I never knew the impact of my words.

Now I do.

The words, "I am" are used 300 times in the Bible.

God said to Moses, "I AM THAT I AM.

This is My name forever, and this is how I am to be remembered in every generation..." (Exodus 3:14)

I strongly believe that we are made in God's image and whatever words follow "I am" we become.

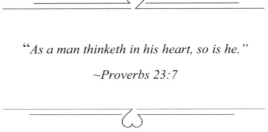

"As a man thinketh in his heart, so is he."

~Proverbs 23:7

This is a belief not only in the Christian faith, but in many other faiths and from spiritual leaders, as well.

Crippling thoughts mixed with negative angry words can increase dis-ease in the body. The results are higher levels of stress and cortisol which influence our attitude and thus, our outcome.

Just how many of our thoughts are negative?

In 2005, the National Science Foundation published an article summarizing research on human thoughts. It was found that the average person has about 12,000 to 60,000 thoughts per day. Of those thousands of thoughts, 80% were negative, and 95% of those were exactly the same repetitive thoughts as the day before.

Studies have shown that there is a fundamental link between thoughts and stress levels we experience, and that taking charge of your mind has positive effects on your overall health, recovery, and well-being.

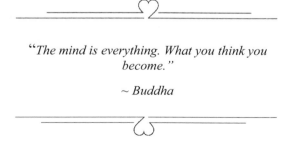

"The mind is everything. What you think you become."

~ Buddha

We see the effects of "belief" in the placebo effect. What is a placebo? It is anything that seems to be a "real" medical treatment but isn't. Research shows that placebo effects are attributable to the brain–mind responses to the context in which a treatment is delivered rather than to the specific actions of the drug.

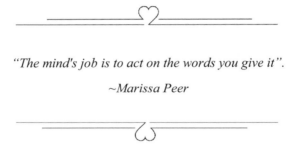

"The mind's job is to act on the words you give it".

~Marissa Peer

How powerful is "belief" or the placebo effect?

Science has shown that under the right circumstances, a placebo can have just as much effect as traditional treatments especially in the area of pain management.

Can the placebo effect and our beliefs about ourselves influence the body's general health or even the benefits of exercise? Maybe.

One such experiment included the housekeeping attendants for a hotel. These hotel attendants believed that they were not getting enough exercise daily to improve their health, and many believed that they didn't exercise at all.

The surgeon general recommends at least 30 minutes per day of physical exercise to maintain a healthy lifestyle. On average, hotel attendees clean 15 rooms per day. Each room can take 20 - 30 minutes to complete.

The hotel room attendants were put into a treatment group and were told that their work provided the recommended exercise for a healthy lifestyle.

Over a four-week period the results were pretty eye opening. The attendants that were in the treatment group lost weight; their body fat percentages, waist-to-hip ratios, and systolic blood pressures dropped. Attendants in the controlled group who believed they did not meet the exercise requirements showed no such improvement. These changes occurred, despite the fact that the hotel room attendants 'amount of work, amount of exercise outside of work, and diets stayed the same.

The Latin meaning for placebo means "I will please." When you understand and grasp the concept that the mind's job is to act on the words you give it, you can dramatically change your life. Your mind works to please you. To do what you instruct it to do. Your words are your body's own Commander in Chief, and the body behaves as it is told.

———————

Thoughts have power.

———————

Every minute of every day your body is physically reacting and changing in response to the thoughts that run through your mind.

It's been shown over and over again that just thinking about something can cause your brain to release neurotransmitters, chemical messengers that allow it to communicate with parts of itself and your nervous system. Neurotransmitters control virtually all of your body's functions, from hormones to digestion to feeling happy, sad, or stressed. (excerpt from Huffpost, "How Your Thoughts Change Your Brain Cells and Genes.")

One important way we can influence our thoughts, which eventually affects our body, is through meditation. Countless studies have shown that meditation slows the rate of cellular aging and reduces cognitive stress.

Meditative practices appear to improve the endocrine balance toward positive arousal (high DHEA, lower cortisol) and decrease oxidative stress. Thus, meditation practices may promote mitotic cell longevity, both through decreasing stress hormones and oxidative stress and increasing hormones that may protect the telomere. This further shows that our thoughts can directly influence our body, both positively and negatively.

Even just a few minutes a day of meditation can restore your inner calm and soothe stress.

Another way to influence our body is through our spoken words.

I distinctly remember the first time I saw the impact of a client's words on the outcome of their body treatments. We had two subjects come in for treatment. They were best friends, but with distinctively different attitudes. Client A had the dream attitude. She came in bubbly, excited and proclaiming to everyone that she was going to have the best results ever. Her best friend, Client B, had a less than desirable attitude. She came in grim, skeptical, and critical. She proclaimed her disbelief in holistic practices out loud to everyone and did not think anything could help her. I carefully measured each of them by making a mark on the front, back, and each side of their waist, abs and upper hip to maintain accuracy of the measurements.

Upon completion of their treatments, I was amazed at what transpired. Client A lost a combined amount of over 4 inches, which was the most I had ever seen in a single treatment! Meanwhile, her negative friend lost just what I expected, zero. She almost seemed proud that she had proven it would not work for her.

It was the first of our in-house experiments, and across the board, we have found that the clients who express their belief that they will have positive results in whatever treatments they choose, will always have better outcomes than the clients who are skeptical and critical.

It seems that just changing your thoughts and affirming your beliefs can actually

manifest either positive or negative results in the body.

The power of the words you say and how you fill in the blank, "I am _____" appears to have a major impact on health and your life.

When I decided to start a supplement company in 2019, we made a decision to prominently place "I am" affirmations on each and every label. As part of a daily regimen of healthy supplements when you reach for any of our supplements, we encourage you to speak the affirmations on the bottle out loud, allowing the brain to hear the power of your words and command your body and mind to optimum health and vitality.

Here are a few affirmations that we use on the Confidence by Char supplement labels to get you started:

" I am confident"

My body is a masterpiece getting stronger day by day

I look in the mirror and I value what I see

When I walk down the street people are inspired by me

I am strong

I stand tall

I am confident

"I am youthful"

I move with ease and flexibility

I am hydrated, refreshed and full of life energy

When I enter a room, people notice the light inside of me

I am bright

I am playful

I am youthful

"I am centered"

I flow through the day on wings of grace

My focus is sharp

My words like poetry

Even in silence my presence is felt

I am calm

I am dynamic

I am centered

I encourage you to continue the list by writing in powerful phrases that you want to become. Repeat them daily. Consider making a recording and playing before bedtime or during meditation. You have the power and the power is yours.

Jesus said, "Truly I tell you, if you have faith like a grain of mustard seed, you can say to this mountain, 'Move from here to there,' and it will move. Nothing will be impossible for you."

~Mathew 17:20

Foundation #7 - 10 Ingredient Age-Defying Recipe

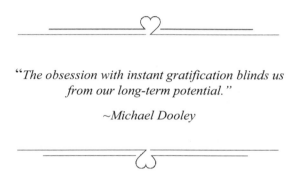

"The obsession with instant gratification blinds us from our long-term potential."

~Michael Dooley

We are a data driven society.

Technology is causing our patience to erode at an accelerated rate.

According to an article featured in ZDnet, a new study says it takes only 16 seconds for us to express frustration if our TV or tablet isn't streaming a movie properly or a web page to load, 25 seconds for a traffic light to change, 20 seconds for the ink to dry on a greeting card, and 18 seconds to lose our cool looking for a pen. We will wait 2.8 days for online delivery to arrive and 3.7 days for handwritten mail to arrive. We are happy waiting on a meal at a restaurant for 14 minutes before seriously testing our patience and 7 minutes to wait for a drink at a pub.

Our impatience due to technology has driven us to believe that instant is the norm. However, in the realm of youthful preservation, "instant" is replaced by consistency and prevention.

✓ We want to be young NOW.

✓ We want smooth skin NOW.

✓ We want to be lean NOW.

✓ We want the perfect body and skin in an instant.

Our thirst for the instant youthful body drives us to extreme measure and fuels the world's obsession with plastic surgery and other quick fixes. We search for the perfect pill, the perfect injection, the best doctor, the latest laser, the fastest workout and the list goes on and on.

But that's not how it works.

As with all the foundations in this book they require consistency. Supplementation can be very beneficial but it requires time. It's not a magic pill but instead a building block and part of a recipe especially when we don't always eat as nutritious as we should.

The payoff in the long term can be beneficial. The modalities, treatments and holistic suggestions in this book is part of a "youthful recipe." Each ingredient is important and builds on the other to create your youthful regimen. Leave one or two out and the results will change. Feel free to add more.

Use the ideas in this book as a foundation to begin to build your own youthful regimen to slow the signs of aging. Think of this as your own unique recipe for vitality. As technology increases, we are finding more and more ways to hack the body promoting longevity and giving a youthful look to the body.

In this section, we will cover just a few of my favorite ingredients and supplements. There are literally hundreds of new ideas and products that are being introduced to the market. Stay up to date on our favorites by joining our Facebook group, Confidence by Char. We will consistently update you on new product formulations and ideas for you to explore that will inspire more confidence in the body and mind. Here are a few of my favorite ingredients to consider for youthful looking skin on the body, enhancing and supporting your diet and exercise efforts, working on your mind to calm stress and reduce inflammation, and strengthening your immune system.

#1. Collagen Peptides

Collagen is sometimes called the body's scaffolding. It is the glue that holds the body together. Collagen is the protein that is responsible for the skin's elasticity. As we age, our bodies produce less of it which causes the skin to sag and wrinkle, our joints to become stiff, and our ligaments and tendons to become less fluid. Our hair follicles weaken, and we lose the luster of our hair and the dewiness of our skin.

In a study in the Journal of Medical Nutrition and Nutraceuticals, several women drank a mixture containing various vitamins, minerals, hydrolyzed collagen, and hyaluronic acid. The results were reduction in the depth of wrinkles, increased hydration and skin elasticity.

When you consume collagen rich in amino acids, your body can break them down for keratin, the protein that makes up hair. Collagen can promote healthy looking hair and may strengthen the hair follicle.

Some studies have shown collagen having a positive effect on arthritis and wound healing.

There are mixed opinions on collagen and its effectiveness.

One of the biggest myths in our industry is the belief that collagen supplements don't work because collagen gets broken down in our digestive tract - or 'destroyed 'by our stomach acid. This "myth" is perpetuated by the un-informed doctors. They are right and wrong.

It is true that the collagen molecule in its native state is too large to be absorbed by the intestine. However, hydrolyzed collagen, which is made by purifying and breaking down amino acids into low-molecular-weight fragments, are small enough to be absorbed through the small intestine and then into the bloodstream. There is also agglomerated collagen. Agglomerated collagen is simply the highest quality protein available. Agglomerated collagen means that it is the most biologically active and in the most absorbable form and mixes easily.

I love drinking this every single day. It's virtually odorless, tasteless and has a nice punch of protein to add to my diet with hardly any calories. I look for agglomerated collagen. Not all collagen is the same, thus the variance in prices. There are different grades, types, and forms. We combine our high-quality collagen with hyaluronic acid to further assist with hydration of the skin. I recommend and love our product called "i am youthful" which also uses Oligopeptides as a key ingredient.

Our "I am youthful" collagen also contains CTGF (Connective Tissue Growth Factors) - peptides that promote collagen accumulation in the body and EGF (Epidermal Growth Factors) - which are polypeptides that promote skin tissue growth and development as well as healing. In addition, the Oligopeptides used in "i am youthful" have been clinically tested to increase longevity, gut bacteria regeneration, and activation of fibroblast growth factor receptors that normalize and stabilize cellular processes. Recommended use: 1 scoop daily with water or liquid of your choice.

#2. Ashwaghanda

Ashwagandha is classified as an adaptogen. Adaptogens works to counteract the effects of stress in the body.

Studies on animals and isolated neuronal cells have revealed that adaptogens exhibit neuroprotective, anti-fatigue, anti-depressive, anxiolytic, nootropic and CNS (central nervous system) stimulating activity.

Ashwagandha has been used for millennia as a rasayana, or a "life extender" in Ayurvedic medicine. Ayurvedic medicine is one of the world's oldest holistic (whole body) healing systems. The practice of Ayurveda originated in India over 5000 years ago. It is sometimes called the "mother of all healings."

Extracts from Ashwagandha root may significantly increase telomerase activity, thereby protecting against telomere loss and potentially delaying aging, suggests a recent cell study.

Telomeres are the caps at the end of each strand of DNA that protect our chromosomes, like the plastic tips at the end of shoelaces. Without the coating, shoelaces become frayed until they can no longer do their job, just as without telomeres, DNA strands become damaged and our cells can't do their job.

Telomeres are shortened as we age but can also be shortened due to stress, obesity, lack of exercise and a poor diet. A recent study showed ashwagandha root extract powder can increase telomerase activity by up to 45%.

Stress and cortisol can also affect telomere length.

In addition, when cortisol levels are too high it affects your body's ability to lose weight and your ability to sleep.

Taking a high quality ashwagandha root extract can dramatically reduce your cortisol levels after only 8 weeks of supplementation. Using ashwagandha has also been effective in decreasing stress and insomnia after 60 days. We use only the highest concentration, most bioavailable full spectrum ashwagandha on the market today in our "I am centered" supplement for hormone and stress support.

#3. Capsicum Fruit Extract

Capsicum comes from hot peppers. The hotter the pepper the more capsicum it has in it.

It activates the sympathetic nervous system that is associated with thermogenesis, which speeds the body's oxidation of fat. Capsicum may increase the body's ability to burn excess fat and break it down into energy when paired with exercise. In some studies, it has even been shown to decrease appetite.

Taking capsicum can cause a burning sensation similar to heartburn. Sometimes the effects of this are very unpleasant and can cause many to stop taking the supplement.

We use a form of capsicum that does not produce the unpleasant burning sensation but yields all the positive results you would want.

We recommend taking about 100 mg of the extract, which is found in our "i am confident" fat burner, at least one hour before exercising. Focus on exercises that build lean muscle, which further burns fat. For a powerful combination, schedule regular Bodicurrent™ treatments to supplement your regular exercise routine and support ATP production in the body.

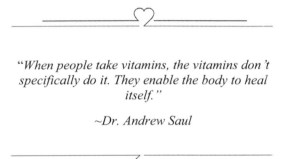

"When people take vitamins, the vitamins don't specifically do it. They enable the body to heal itself."

~Dr. Andrew Saul

#4. Coenzyme Q10

Coenzyme Q10 (CoQ10) is a naturally occurring nutrient in the body and is found in a plethora of foods. As our bodies age, we produce less CoQ10 so it becomes important to supplement.

CoQ10 is a vital part of the anti-aging equation because it acts like an antioxidant by protecting cellular damage and plays an important part in metabolism.

This nutrient is made and stored in the magical mitochondria. Mitochondria are known as the powerhouses of the cell. They are organelles that act like a digestive system which takes in nutrients, breaks them down, and creates energy rich molecules for the cell. Without CoQ10, the level of ATP that the mitochondria produce drops, the energy that is available to that tissue decreases, and dysfunction and health conditions can potentially develop.

CoQ10 is instrumental in supporting the mitochondrial function.

CoQ10 has been shown to help improve heart health and blood sugar regulation, assist in the prevention and treatment of cancer and reduce the frequency of migraines. It could also reduce the oxidative damage that leads to muscle fatigue, skin damage and brain and lung diseases.

Health conditions like heart disease, brain disorders, diabetes, and cancer have been linked to low levels of CoQ10.
It is not clear whether low levels of CoQ10 cause these diseases or are a result of them.

CoQ10 also plays a significant role in boosting the immune system.

Cells involved in immune function are highly energy-dependent making CoQ10 a major player in immune support.

I personally take 200mg of CoQ10 daily and is hands down one of my favorite supplements. I feel it is essential for maintaining youthfulness at a cellular level.

#5. Green Tea Extract

Green tea is known as a superfood mainly because of it EGCG content. Epigallocatechin gallate (EGCG) is a unique plant compound that gets a lot of attention for its potential positive impact on health.

Catechin polyphenols, including EGCG, have been associated with antioxidant, anti-inflammatory and anti-mutagenic effects. Catechins are thought to prevent weight gain by promoting greater energy expenditure and fat oxidation.

Green tea has also been shown to have positive effect on brain health, memory and can be beneficial to skin health.
EGCG exists in small amount in many plant-based foods like strawberries and avocados and some nuts.

The standardized amount of polyphenols in green tea extract are 50%. We use green tea extract, 98% polyphenols in our supplement called, "I am confident" as part of our proprietary blend for weight management.

#6. Glutathione

Glutathione (GSH) is the most powerful antioxidant in the body and recharges other antioxidants. It is referred to as the mother of all antioxidants, the master detoxifier and support for the immune system. Antioxidants are substances that may protect your cells against free radicals.

Your body is capable of making its own Glutathione but everything from poor diet, pollution, toxins, stress and a host of diseases depletes it. Glutathione is also capable of preventing damage on a cellular level from free radicals and heavy metals. It can reduce cell damage in alcoholic and nonalcoholic fatty liver disease and may fight against autoimmune disease.

Studies show that low glutathione levels are also associated with less fat burning and higher rates of fat storing in the body.

#7. Tremella Mushroom

Tremella mushroom is another superfood and longevity inducing herb used in Chinese medicine. Also known as a snow mushroom, it has been an integral ingredient in skincare for thousands of years. In ancient times, like many of the other revered medicinal mushrooms such as reishi and cordyceps, tremella was only reserved for royalty, or for elite people who could afford this highly valued superfood.

Tremella mushroom has many restorative benefits but it is most famous for its beauty and skin enhancing properties. In ancient China, Yang Guifei (719-756, Tang Dynasty) was one of the "Four Great Beauties", an imperial concubine that is considered one of the most beautiful women in Chinese history.

She was so beautiful that she was referred to as having "a face that would put flowers to shame." It was reported that Yang Guifei used tremella mushroom to maintain her glowing complexion and youthful skin.

For centuries, Chinese women have been consuming tremella in its whole mushroom form and as an extract to make their skin more moist, soft and pliable. It's recognized as one of the best tonic herbs to help maintain the health of the skin as the body ages.

#8. Pearl Powder

Pearl powder is a superfood from the sea. Pearls are known for their iridescent beauty and ornamental use for stunning jewelry but the Daoists of ancient China prized them for other reasons. The only empress in Chinese history, Wu Zetian, used it because of its beauty and properties. Emperors and empresses alike used the precious treasure for medicinal and beauty effects on the body and skin.

Pearl powder holds promise for its longevity benefits both externally and on a cellular level. Nacre, an ingredient in pearl powder, can stimulate fibroblasts in the body which accelerates wound healing and helps collagen regenerate itself. More collagen regeneration can make the skin look more luminous, bouncy, and young and help to make wrinkles less apparent.

Bioactivities associated with nacre holds potential in the development of therapeutics for bone regeneration and against oxidative stress induced cell damage.

Pearl powder is made by boiling fresh or saltwater pearls and then milling the pearls into a soft fine powder that's similar in texture to flour or cornstarch.

Pearl powder contains high levels of amino acids, trace minerals, calcium and antioxidant boosters. It is said to boost superoxide dismutase (SOD) and glutathione which can fight off disease and may even extend life.

Pearl has magnesium in it which can help with depression, anxiety, and mood.

Pearl powder is used in a variety of ways from supplements to skin care products. Whatever form you choose to use we see it as treasure from the sea for your regimen for a youthful looking face and body. We like it internally rather than just as a skin care product. We feel this is the best way for your entire body to benefit from its magic.

#9. Sea Buckthorn oil

Sea Buckthorn oil is rich in various vitamins, minerals and beneficial plant compounds and has an abundance of active compounds.

Sea Buckthorn oil may benefit a healthy heart, improving blood cholesterol levels and protect against blood clots. It can protect your skin when applied directly. Sea

Buckthorn oil may boost your immune system and contribute to a healthy liver.

Sea buckthorn may reduce vaginal drying and act as an effective alternative treatment for postmenopausal women who cannot take estrogen. It can improve overall vaginal health.

Feeling youthful doesn't stop at the way you look externally. It not only involves the mind and body but also your sensuality. For women approaching menopause or for those of us who are already post-menopausal, feeling youthful also means how sensual we feel. Vaginal dryness can put a halt on your playfulness and desire to have sex and make you feel less than your younger counterparts. This may be in part because of the "feel good" hormone release of serotonin. Having sex can make us look, act and feel younger and stronger.

As a woman over 55, I'm here to inspire "the more experienced women" of my generation and beyond. Feel great about your age. Older women can be incredibly desirable as they hold a playbook of moves that can't be matched. The only barrier to this plethora of fun is the dreaded vaginal atrophy and dryness that can occur. Prescription medication can contain estrogen and other synthetic ingredients that I just don't want to put in the "ethereal flower." An incredible alternative is sea buckthorn oil.

Sea Buckthorn oil has shown beneficial effects on vaginal health, indicating it is a potential alternative for mucosal integrity for those women not able to use estrogen treatment for vaginal atrophy.

#10. CBD Oil

You can't deny the frenzy around CBD or cannabidiol. It's a natural remedy that seems to compete with some major prescription drugs. CBD is extracted from the hemp plant or marijuana. Hemp plants are cannabis plants that contain less than 0.3 percent THC, while marijuana plants are cannabis plants that contain higher concentrations of THC. THC, or tetrahydrocannabinol, is the chemical responsible for most of marijuana's psychological effects. CBD is a non-psychoactive compound. That means it doesn't produce the "high" associated with THC. CBD is sold in the form of gels, gummies, oils, supplements, extracts, and more.

Some of the touted health benefits are:

1.	Relieving Pain

2.	Reducing anxiety and depression

3.	Anti-inflammatory

4.	May have neuroprotective properties

5.	Could benefit heart health

6.	Positive effects on the skin and many other possible benefits

CBD has caused sort of a "gold rush" mentality, some hype but some real beneficial effects. I am a firm believer and user of high-quality CBD products. I like organic, full spectrum CBD oil from a reliable source from the United States. My favorite oils are grown and produced in Colorado.

The price range of CBD oil is vast. It's important you know where your product is farmed. The hemp plant kind of acts like a vacuum in the soil, sucking up these toxins such as:

➤ Heavy Metals

➤ Radioactive Elements

➤ Pesticides, Herbicides, and Fungicides

➤ Explosives

➤ Fuels

Also affecting the price of these oils are the extraction methods used. The cheapest way to extract the oil is using toxic solvents that are dangerous to our health such as propane, hexane, pentane and butane. I highly recommend you steer clear of these methods.

Some companies use organic, pharmaceutical-grade ethanol to process the CBD. This is considered an effective way to remove the toxins and can yield a higher concentration of CBD and is better than using toxic solvents.

Another method is CO_2 extraction using carbon dioxide under high pressure in an extremely cold environment. Supercritical CO_2 extraction requires expensive equipment, more complex refinement process and production expertise, but it ensures that CBD oil maintains its purity all through the process. CO_2 is a natural occurring compound and is labeled safe by the FDA for industrial extractions.

My personal recommendation is cold pressed extraction. Just like when producing olive oil, cold press involves minimal heat, no toxic solvents, or other unnecessary chemicals. I believe that the way the oil is extracted not only affects the taste but also the integrity of the oil and how it reacts in the body.

In conclusion, knowing the source, the extraction method, where it's farmed and buying from a trusted retailer is imperative. Don't shop for the cheapest retailer online.

Do your homework to find the highest quality, organically farmed CBD and know the extraction method.

For more information on products that contain the ingredients discussed in this chapter, please log onto www.confidencebychar.com click on the shop now tab. For Bodicurrent™ treatments available in your area, click on the locator tab to find trained practitioners at wellness centers and luxury spas nationwide.

Your Prescription For Youth

"There is a foundation of youth: it is your mind, your talents, the creativity you bring to your life and the lives of people you love. When you learn to tap this source you will truly have defeated age."

~Sophia Loren

Confidence is all in the mind.

Master the mind and the body will follow.

The following suggestions are just the basics.

As your quest to become the best version of you emerges, you will add more to your recipe for being seen.

Here are the foundational pillars of youthfulness to get you started.

1.   **Move your body**. Do something you love like dancing, yoga, lifting or just a walk in the park. Each and every day take advantage of your healthy body. If you are healthy enough to move, find gratitude and joy in that and move daily. Supplement your exercise with microcurrent frequencies by incorporating the Bodicurrent™ signature treatment to increase your ATP production and cellular health. This supports the body's ability to heal and stay youthful. Bodicurrent™ treatments, in my opinion, are

the most groundbreaking, easy, safe, holistic body hack for youthful preservation that you can find.

2.   **Hydration**. The most cost-effective youthful preserving "body hack" there is. Easy and accessible.

3.   **Manage your fat, don't destroy it**. Fat is an organ and has a major purpose in your body. You don't have to be a size two but consider making healthy choices and treat your body like a priceless treasure by giving it the best possible care in all areas.

4.   **Introduce your body to alternative modalities**. Try modalities like LED light therapy for increased collagen production and beautification of the skin, infrared saunas for detoxification and cryotherapy to increase the body's production of brown fat and thermogenesis and of course the ever popular Bodicurrent™ treatments.

5.   **Consider Fasting as a longevity hack**. Make sure you are in good health or get clearance from your doctor before attempting fasting. Educate yourself on safe practices and seek a professional to guide you through the process.

6.   **Manage your Mind**. Where the mind goes the body follows. Feed your brain with the directions and commands that you want it to follow knowing that you have that power. You can either choose to command your body and your future to health and prosperity or curse your body and your future to defeat. Daily practice of meditation, positive affirmations and visualizations are extremely effective.

7.   **Incorporate supplements**. Choose the highest quality ingredients and products that you can afford. Invest in your body with supplements that contain antioxidants, anti-

inflammatories, immune system support and potentially life extending ingredients.

A few final thoughts.

Surround yourself with the people and experiences you love.

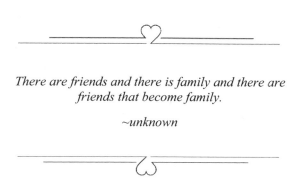

There are friends and there is family and there are friends that become family.

~unknown

It's imperative to find your community of support. When you don't feel confident, find someone who believes in you. They hold space for you until you can step into your strength.

There is no doubt in my mind that a key to my physical and emotional healing were my friends who gathered around me after my husband's death, the accident, the creation of a new life and a new business. They were instrumental in giving me the strength to carry on when all I wanted to do was disappear. They inspired me to live and become healthier every day.

My friends and family are the wings that have given my dreams and life flight. Without them I would never be who I am or where I am today. I am eternally grateful.

You become what you surround yourself with.

Live well.

Nothing replaces or shows up more on the body than the evidence of living well.

Belly laugh often.

Dare to live life full out.

Dare to love unconditionally knowing it may not be returned in the same capacity.

Dare to take risks, that is where the juiciness of life lives and lastly,

DARE TO BE SEEN.

Never sit in the darkness UNLESS you are there to shine your light.

I see you and I cannot wait to meet you in person!

Love,

ABOUT THE AUTHOR

Char Fontanills is the founder of Confidence by Char, the brand behind every beautiful body.

Char has over 30 years in the beauty industry and over 20 years in the financial markets.
She is an author, world class speaker, avid investor and innovator of products, services and events that inspire confidence of the mind and body.

Char is the creator of the Bodicurrent (tm) protocol which uses proprietary Microcurrent frequencies to amplify cellular health, performance and body beautification.

In 2015 she took bold steps to build a company that is committed to bringing breakthrough technology and luxury products to the wellness community. She is known for her "Dare To Be Seen" campaign which encourages women to treat their bodies as the masterpiece that it is and to never shy from standing out.

In 2019 she expanded her influence by launching her luxury "i am" supplement line featuring exceptional ingredients and powerful affirmations on every bottle.

Char's passion for "body hacks" led her to become a Certified Bulletproof Coach with the Human Potential Institute. She is also a certified RTT Rapid Transformation Therapy Practitioner under the world-renowned Marissa Peer. Char specializes in guiding groups through visualization and meditation techniques to uncover limiting beliefs and replace them with powerful commands that shift the mindset to have audacious confidence.

Confidence Retreats and intimate summits around the world set the stage for transformation at every level. To have Char speak at your next event or to find out more about any of the Confidence products or services, visit our website at www.confidencebychar.com.

Bibliography and References

Tara, S. (2016) *The Secret Life of Fat* W.W. Norton and Company

Plante, A. (02/ 2016). *How the Human Body Uses Electricity*. Retrieved from http://www.graduate.umaryland.edu

Electrotherapy: cosmetic Retrieved from https://en.wikipedia.org/wiki/Electrotherapy_(cosmet ic)

Mitochondria: Turning on the Powerhouse Retrieved from http://www.biology4kids.com/files/cell_mito.html

Cheng, N., Van Hoof, H., Bockx, E., Hoogmartens, MJ., Mulier, JC., (1982) *The Effects of Electric Currents on ATP Generation, Protein Synthesis, and Membrane Transport of Rat Skin* Retrieved from https://www.ncbi.nlm.nih.gov/pubmed/7140077

Mahmoud, A., Kazzam, E., Amir, N., Nyberg, F., Adem, A. (2013) *Effects of Dehydration and Blockade of Angiotensis II AT1 Receptor on Stress Hormones and Anti-Oxidants in the One-Humped Camel* Retrieved from https://www.ncbi.nlm.nih.gov/pmc/articles/PMC4225509/

Shaw, G. (n.d.) *Water and Stress Reduction: Sipping Stress Away* Retrieved from https://www.webmd.com/diet/features/water-stress-reduction#1

Popkin, B., D'Anci, K., Rosenberg, I. (2010) *Water, Hydration and Health* Retrieved from https://www.ncbi.nlm.nih.gov/pmc/articles/PMC2908954/

The Water in You: Water and the Human Body
Retrieved from https://www.usgs.gov/special-topic/water-science-school/science/water-you-water-and-human-body?qt-science_center_objects=0#qt-science_center_objects

Adipose Tissue Retrieved from
https://www.britannica.com/science/adipose-tissue

Marcin, A. (1/22/18) *Brown Fat:What you Should Know* Retrieved from:
https://www.healthline.com/health/brown-fat#1

Infrared Sauna Health Benefits Retrieved from:
https://infraredsauna.com/infrared-sauna-health-benefits/

For more information about Sunlighten check out their website https://www.sunlighten.com.

Loap, S., Lathe, R. (5/2/2018) *Mechanism Underlying Tissue Cryotherapy to Combat Obesity/Overweight: Triggering Thermogene*sis Retrieved from https://www.ncbi.nlm.nih.gov/pmc/articles/PMC5954 866/

Lombardi, G., Ziemann, G., Banfi., G. (5/2/2017) *Whole Body Cryotherapy in Athletes: From Therapy to Stimulation. An Updated Review of the Literature* Retrieved from https://www.ncbi.nlm.nih.gov/pmc/articles/PMC5411 446/

Rymaszewska, J., Ramsey, D., Chladzinska-Kiejna, S. (2/5/2008) *Whole-Body Cryotherapy as Adjunct Treatment of Depressive and Anxiety Disorders* Retrieved from https://www.ncbi.nlm.nih.gov/pmc/articles/PMC2734 249/

Torgan, C. (7/28/2014) *Cool Temperature Alters Human Fat and Metabolism* Retrieved from https://www.nih.gov/news-events/nih-research-matters/cool-temperature-alters-human-fat-metabolism

Brandhorst, S., Longo, D. (11/15/2019) *Protein Quantity and Source, Fasting-Mimicking Diets, and Longevity* Retrieved from https://www.ncbi.nlm.nih.gov/pmc/articles/PMC6855936/

Yang, Z., Klionsky, D. (9/12/2010) *Eaten Alive: A History of Macroautophagy* Retrieved from https://www.ncbi.nlm.nih.gov/pmc/articles/PMC3616322/

Fung, J., Moore, J. (2016) *The Complete Guide to Fasting* Victory Belt Publishing

Engert, V., Smallwood, J., Singer, T. (2014) *Mind your Thoughts: Associations Between Self-Generated Thoughts and Stress-induced and Baseline Levels of Cortisol and Alpha-amylase.* Retrieved from https://www.ncbi.nlm.nih.gov/pubmed/25457636

Wager, D., Atlas, L (July 2015) *The Neuroscience of Placebo Effects: Connecting Context, Learning and Health* Retrieved from https://www.ncbi.nlm.nih.gov/pmc/articles/PMC6013051/

Crum, A., Langer, E. (2007) *Mind-set Matters:Exercise and the PlaceboEffect* Retrieved from
https://www.ncbi.nlm.nih.gov/pubmed/17425538

Hampton, D. (2016) *How Your Thoughts Change Your Brain, Cells and Genes* Retrieved from
https://www.huffpost.com/entry/how-your-thoughts-change-your-brain-cells-and-genes_b_9516176

Epel, E., Daubenmier, J., Moskowitz, J., Folkman, S., Blackburn, E. (2009) *Can Meditation Slow Rate of Cellular Aging?* Retrieved from
https://www.ncbi.nlm.nih.gov/pmc/articles/PMC3057175/

(2019) *The Power of the Placebo Effect* Retrieved from https://www.health.harvard.edu/mental-health/the-power-of-the-placebo-effect

Matyszczyk, C. (2019) *Technology is Making Us More Impatient, Says Study* Retrieved from
https://www.zdnet.com/article/technology-is-making-us-more-impatient-says-study/

Anderer, J. (2019) *Hurry Up: Modern Patience Thresholds Lower Than Ever Before, Technology to Blame* Retrieved by https://www.studyfinds.org/hurry-up-modern-patience-thresholds-lower-than-ever-before-survey-finds/

Choi, FD., Sung, CT., Juhasz, ML., Mesinkovsk, NA. (2019) *Oral Collagen Supplementation: A Systematic Review of Dermatological Applications* Retrieved from https://www.ncbi.nlm.nih.gov/pubmed/30681787

Panossian, A., Wikman, G., (2010) *Effects of Adaptogens on the Central Nervous System and the Molecular Mechanisms Associated with Their Stress* Retrieved from https://www.ncbi.nlm.nih.gov/pmc/articles/PMC3991026/

Raguraman VR, Subramaniam JR. (2016) *Withania somnifera Root Extract Enhances Telomerase Activity in the Human HeLa Cell Line.* Retrieved from https://www.scirp.org/journal/paperinformation.aspx?paperid=65533

Neubert, A. (2011) *Study: Reasonable Quantities of Red Pepper May Help Curb Appetite* Retrieved from https://www.purdue.edu/newsroom/research/2011/11 0425MattesPepper.htm

Galluzzi L1, Kepp O, Trojel-Hansen C, Kroemer G. (2012) *Mitochondrial Control of Cellular Life, Stress, and Death* Retrieved from https://www.ncbi.nlm.nih.gov/pubmed/23065343

Saini, R. (2011) *Coenzyme Q10:the Essential Ingredient* Retrieved from https://www.ncbi.nlm.nih.gov/pmc/articles/PMC3178 961/

DiNicolantonio JJ1, Bhutani J2, McCarty MF3, O'Keefe JH1. (2015) *Coenzyme Q10 for the treatment of heart failure: a review of the literature.* Retrieved from https://www.ncbi.nlm.nih.gov/pubmed/26512330

Cooke, M., Iosa, M., Beford, T., Shelmadine, B., Hudson, G., Kerksick, C., Kreidir, R. (2008) *Effects of acute and 14-day Coenzyme Q10 Supplementation on Exercise Performance in Both Trained and Untrained Individuals.* Retrieved from https://www.ncbi.nlm.nih.gov/pubmed/18318910/

Mandel, S., Weinreib, O., Amit., T., Youdim, MB. (2004) *Cell signaling pathways in the neuroprotective actions of the green tea polyphenol (-)-epigallocatechin-3-gallate: implications for neurodegenerative diseases.* Retrieved from: https://www.ncbi.nlm.nih.gov/pubmed/15009657

Bhullar, K., Rupasinghe, H. (2013) *Polyphenols:Multipotent Therapeutic Agents in Neurodegenerative Diseases* Retrieved from https://www.ncbi.nlm.nih.gov/pmc/articles/PMC3690243/

Hodgson, A., Randell, R., Jeukendrup, A. (2013) *The Effect of Green Tea Extract on Fat Oxidation* Retrieved from https://www.ncbi.nlm.nih.gov/pmc/articles/PMC3649093/

Cory, H., Passarelli, S., Szeto, J., Tamez, M., Mattei, J. (2018) *The Role of Polyphenols in Human Health and Food Systems: A Mini-Review* Retrieved from https://www.ncbi.nlm.nih.gov/pmc/articles/PMC6160559/

Goutzourelas, N., Orfanou, M., Charizanis, I., Leon, G., Spandidos, D., Kouretas, D. (2018) *GSH Levels Affect Weight Loss in Individuals with Metabolic Syndrome and Obesity FollowingDietary Therapy* Retrieved from https://www.ncbi.nlm.nih.gov/pmc/articles/PMC6090313/

Yang Guifei Retrieved from https://en.wikipedia.org/wiki/Yang_Guifei

Li, YC., Chen, CR., Young, TH (2013) *Pearl Extract Enhances the Migratory Ability of Fibroblasts in a Wound Healing Model* Retrieved from https://www.ncbi.nlm.nih.gov/pubmed/23043617

Chaturvedi, R., Singha, P., Dey., S. (2013) *Water Soluble Bioactives of Nacre Mediate Antioxidant Activity and Osteoblast Differentiation* Retrieved from https://www.ncbi.nlm.nih.gov/pmc/articles/PMC3868599/

Serefko A1, Szopa A, Wlaź P, Nowak G, Radziwoń-Zaleska M, Skalski M, Poleszak E. (2013) *Magnesium in Depression* Retrieved from https://www.ncbi.nlm.nih.gov/pubmed/23950577

Tarleton, EK., Littenberg, B., (2015) *Magnesium Intake and Depression in Adults* Retrieved from https://www.ncbi.nlm.nih.gov/pubmed/25748766

Shults, CW., Oakes, D., , Kieburtz, K. , Beal, MF., Haas, R., Plumb, S., (2002) *Effects of Coenzyme Q10 in Early Parkinson Disease: Evidence of Slowing of the Functional Decline* Retrieved by https://www.ncbi.nlm.nih.gov/pubmed/12374491

Zielinska, A., Nowak, (2017) *Abundance of Active Ingredients in Sea-Buckthorn Oil* Retrieved from https://www.ncbi.nlm.nih.gov/pmc/articles/PMC5438513/

Olas, B., (2018) *The Beneficial Health Aspects of Sea Buckthorn* Retrieved from https://www.ncbi.nlm.nih.gov/pubmed/29166576

Larmo, PS., Yang, B., Hyssala, J., Kallio, HP., Erkkola, R. (2014) *Effects of sea buckthorn oil intake on vaginal atrophy in postmenopausal women: a randomized, double-blind, placebo-controlled study.* Retrieved from https://www.ncbi.nlm.nih.gov/pubmed/25104582

Russo, E. (2008) *Cannibinoids in the Treatment of Difficult to Treat Pain* Retrieved from https://www.ncbi.nlm.nih.gov/pmc/articles/PMC2503660/

Cartwright, C., Gibson, K., Read, J., Cowan, O., Dehar, T. (2016) *Long-Term Antidepressant Use: Patient Perspectives of Benefits and Adverse Effects* Retrieved from https://www.ncbi.nlm.nih.gov/pmc/articles/PMC4970636/

Vuckovik, S., Srebro, D., Vujovik, S., Vucetik, C., Prostran, M. (2018) *Cannabinoids and Pain: New Insights From the Old Molecules* Retrieved from https://www.ncbi.nlm.nih.gov/pmc/articles/PMC6277878/

Maroon, J., Bost, J. (2018) *Review of the Neurological Benefits of Phytocannabinoids* Retrieved from https://www.ncbi.nlm.nih.gov/pmc/articles/PMC5938896/

Stanley, C., Hind, W., O'Sullivan, S. (2012) *Is the Cardiovascular System a Therapeutic Target for Cannibidiol?* Retrieved from https://www.ncbi.nlm.nih.gov/pmc/articles/PMC3579247/

Toth, K., Adam, D., Biro, T., Olah, A. (2019) *Cannabidoid Signaling in the Skin: Therapeutic Potential of the "C(ut) annabidoid System* Retrieved from https://www.ncbi.nlm.nih.gov/pmc/articles/PMC6429381/

Made in the USA
Columbia, SC
25 June 2020

12350396R00124